i

Welcome

She's without doubt the biggest star on the planet, one of the most exciting and innovative artists in the music industry today and loved by millions of us around the world. And with over 150 shows in more than 50 cities across five continents, Taylor Swift's groundbreaking Eras Tour is already one of the biggest and best the world has ever seen. Split into ten distinct acts, it takes fans on an audiovisual adventure through her career so far, from her beginnings as a teen country starlet, to the genre-shifting global sensation she has become.

Now it's time to celebrate her tour de force in creative style! In this book, you can unleash your inner artist and test your Swiftie knowledge. There are 36 Eras Tour-themed illustrations ready for you to customise with colour, plus a selection of fun puzzles to solve and quizzes to answer. So whether you were lucky enough to get tickets for the tour or not, let's grab some colours and get started...

Contents

Colouring

Tick off the ones you've done! ✓

9

11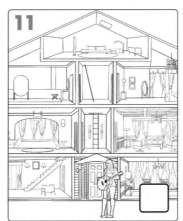

15

17

21

23

25

27

29

33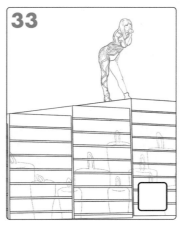

35

37

The Eras Tour is born

After teasing an upcoming tour while promoting her tenth album, *Midnights*, Taylor finally gave us the news we'd all been waiting for. She officially announced her Eras Tour on 1 November 2022 during an appearance on the TV show *Good Morning America* and via social media.

A musical journey

The Eras Tour would be Taylor's sixth concert tour and her biggest to date. Split into ten unique acts, with each celebrating a different "musical era" from Taylor's incredible career, the shows would feature a host of stunning outfits, amazing set design and some of the singer's biggest hits.

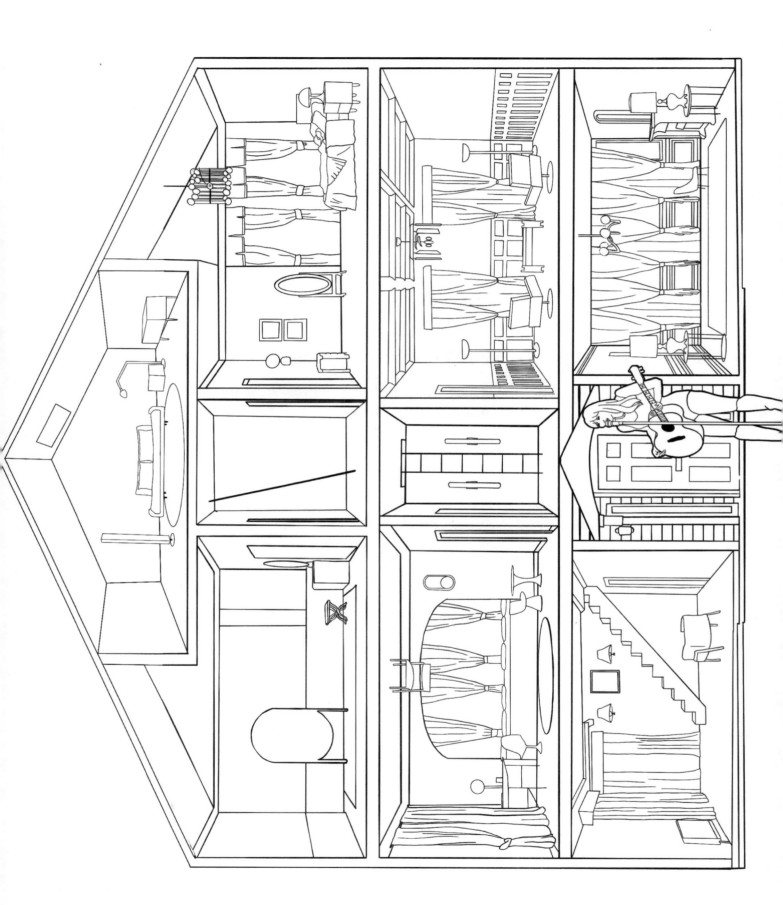

Tour fever

The demand for tickets was unprecedented, with Swifties around the world desperate to get a glimpse of their idol. In the US, more than 2.4 million tickets were sold in the presale alone – the highest by an artist in a single day.

The Lover era

The Eras Tour kicked off in style in Glendale, Arizona, on 17 March 2023. The shows open with the *Lover* era, where Taylor runs through some of her hits from her seventh album, including 'Cruel Summer' and 'You Need to Calm Down'. She dons her iconic bodysuit, pairing it with a sparkly blazer during 'The Man'.

The Fearless era

The *Fearless* act comes next, with Taylor wowing fans with her stunning outfits – shimmering metallic flapper-style dresses in gold and silver. Taylor's parents even helped her recreate the iconic *Fearless* guitar especially for The Eras Tour, decorating it with rhinestones the day before the opening show!

Dress to impress

Not only is Taylor the queen of pop, she's also an undisputed style icon. She's worn more than 40 different outfits so far during The Eras Tour – from bodysuits to ballgowns – and has changed outfits up to an incredible 16 times a night!

Breaking through

It was her second album, *Fearless*, released in 2008, that brought Taylor to mainstream attention for the first time. Three of her hit singles from the Grammy Award-winning album feature in the Eras Tour setlist – 'You Belong with Me', 'Love Story' and the album's title track.

The evermore era

The transition from the *Fearless* act to the *evermore* era is one of the most visually stunning of the whole tour. Sequins and sparkle are replaced by moody, wintery woods and trees that seemingly grow out of the stage, while Taylor stuns either in a cute mustard-yellow dress or an alternate bronze version.

A Swift surprise

Taylor stunned fans in December 2020 with the release of *evermore*, her ninth studio album, which came just five months after sister album *folklore*. Five songs from the indie folk record feature in the Eras Tour setlist, including US No. 1 single 'willow', 'tolerate it', ''tis the damn season' and 'marjorie'.

Mellow yellow

Sticking with the woodland theme, Taylor takes centre stage on a moss-covered piano to perform 'champagne problems'. Murder-mystery tale 'no body, no crime' would make an appearance in place of "tis the damn season' during shows in LA, Seattle and Santa Clara as rock trio HAIM joined Taylor on stage.

The reputation era

The glitz and glamour return with the *reputation* era up next. Taylor takes to the stage in her one and only *reputation* outfit. Designed by Roberto Cavalli, the iconic black one-legged jumpsuit features a bejewelled red snake design that winds from Taylor's leg all the way up to her neck.

Serpent symbolism

From Taylor's outfit to the set design, you may be wondering what's with all the snakes during the *reputation* chapter of The Eras Tour. Well, it all stems from a very public fallout between our favourite singer and Kim Kardashian in 2016, in which KK appeared to refer to Tay as a snake on social media.

Top of the pops

Released in November 2017, *reputation* was Taylor's sixth studio album and her fourth consecutive album to sell one million first-week copies in the US. It also topped charts worldwide. Four songs from the album feature on the Eras Tour setlist, including '...Ready for It?', 'Delicate' and 'Don't Blame Me'.

I ♥ T.S.

Unsurprisingly, 'Look What You Made Me Do', the album's lead single, also makes an appearance on the Eras Tour setlist. In a nod to the song's iconic music video, Taylor's backup dancers perform in doll boxes dressed in outfits inspired by past versions of Taylor.

The Speak Now era

Next up, we're introduced to the fifth act of Taylor's Eras Tour. Released in October 2010, *Speak Now* was Taylor's third studio album and charts her growth from adolescence to adulthood. It was written entirely by Taylor during her Fearless Tour and spent six weeks at No. 1 on the US *Billboard* 200 charts.

Evolving eras

With Taylor's standard setlist originally consisting of 44 of her best-loved songs, each Eras Tour show lasts approximately three-and-a-half hours! However, some *Speak Now* fans were left disappointed that only one song from the album – 'Enchanted' – featured. Always one to keep her Swifties happy, Taylor added fan-favourite 'Long Live' following the release of *Speak Now (Taylor's Version)* in July 2023.

Queen of pop

Beautiful ballgowns are the order of the day for the *Speak Now* era. Performing against a striking purple backdrop, Taylor looks like royalty in stunning gold, silver, blue and baby pink ballgowns as she performs 'Enchanted' and 'Long Live'.

The Red era

The sixth act kicks off with '22' from Taylor's fourth studio album, *Red*. She also runs through the 2012 album's lead single 'We Are Never Ever Getting Back Together' and 'I Knew You Were Trouble'. To the delight of Swifties everywhere, the fabled 10-minute version of 'All Too Well' from the *Red* re-release brings the era to an emotional close.

One big family

In an effort to make Swifties feel even more connected to her Eras Tour shows, fans were given light-up wristbands that flash, pulse and create patterns. Highlighting the positive community vibes, fans have even been making friendship bracelets for each other.

Girl in red

In a throwback to an outfit from the '22' music video, Taylor rocks a series of T-shirts with sequinned slogans – including a twist on the iconic original with 'A Lot Going On At The Moment' and 'Who's Taylor Swift Anyway? Ew'. Beneath the shirts is a stunning red-to-black bodysuit, which she complements with a sparkly red jacket during 'All Too Well' and on the occasions when she performed 'Nothing New' with Phoebe Bridgers.

The folklore era

Released during the pandemic in July 2020, *folklore* was the first of Taylor's surprise indie-folk sister albums and her eighth studio album. The *folklore* act, the seventh of The Eras Tour, sees the return of Taylor's idyllic moss-covered forest cabin that we first saw during the 2021 Grammy Awards.

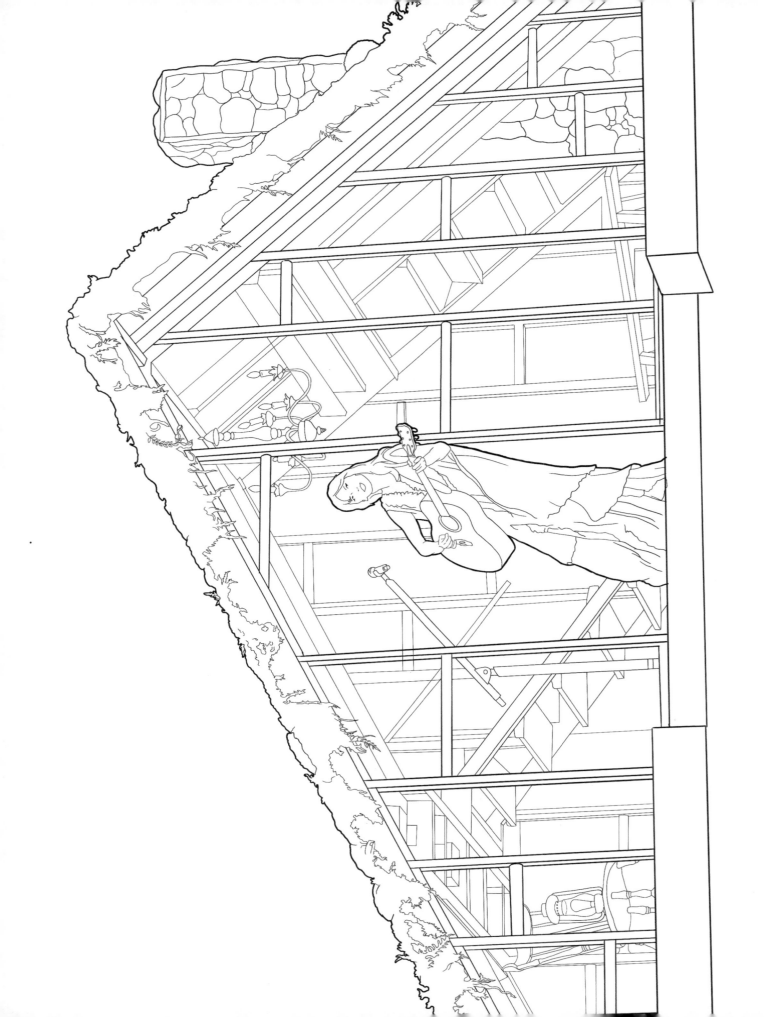

Cottagecore chic

The *folklore* act is all about floaty, textured dresses in a host of muted, natural colours. From Italian dressmaker Alberta Ferretti, Taylor has worn a number of dreamy designs in green, purple, cream and more, which perfectly capture the ethereal aesthetic of this era.

Easter eggs

Swifties have been on the hunt for Taylor's Easter eggs ever since the tour kicked off and they went into a frenzy when, during a performance of 'Bejeweled' from *Midnights*, she included moves from a fan's viral TikTok dance. Who says Taylor doesn't pay attention to her fans?!

Cabin fever

After the spoken-word 'seven', Taylor performs 'the 1' or 'invisible string' while sitting atop her cabin. She then joins her band for 'betty' and 'the last great american dynasty' with her dancers. She works her way through 'august', 'illicit affairs' and 'my tears ricochet' before rounding off the *folklore* set with 'cardigan' at her cabin.

The 1989 era

Considered by many fans and critics to be the best of Taylor's albums to date, *1989* was released in October 2014 and cemented her status as one of pop's biggest superstars. It features some of her biggest and best-loved hits and won Taylor Album of the Year and Best Pop Vocal Album at the 2016 Grammy Awards.

Retro revival

Taylor rocks a sparkly two-piece from designer Roberto Cavalli during the eighth act of her Eras Tour shows. The outfits come in a host of eye-catching colours, from orange and bright green to hot pink. Taylor performs five of her hits from *1989*, including 'Style', 'Bad Blood' and 'Wildest Dreams'.

Taylor's versions

On 9 August 2023, during her show in Inglewood, California, Taylor announced *1989 (Taylor's Version)*, the latest of her re-recorded albums. It followed re-released versions of *Fearless*, *Red* and *Speak Now*. Taylor also used her shows to premiere videos for 'Karma' and 'I Can See You'.

Shake it up

Excitable Swifties literally made the Earth move during the star's shows in Seattle in July 2023, causing seismic activity equal to a 2.3 magnitude earthquake. Fittingly it's thought that it was during *1989*'s 'Shake It Off', as well as 'Blank Space', that the 'Swift Quake' was created.

Surprise songs

To ensure no two Eras Tour shows are the same, Taylor's penultimate act is an acoustic set featuring two surprise songs – one on the piano and one on guitar. Taylor's original plan was to play different surprise songs each night and only to repeat a song if she was unhappy with a previous version.

Taylor's friends

Throughout The Eras Tour, Taylor has been joined on stage by a number of special guests and supporting acts – from Paramore and Gayle, who opened the very first show of the tour, to Sabrina Carpenter, Phoebe Bridgers, HAIM and more. At the shows in East Rutherford, Taylor brought out rapper Ice Spice to perform their 'Karma' remix together.

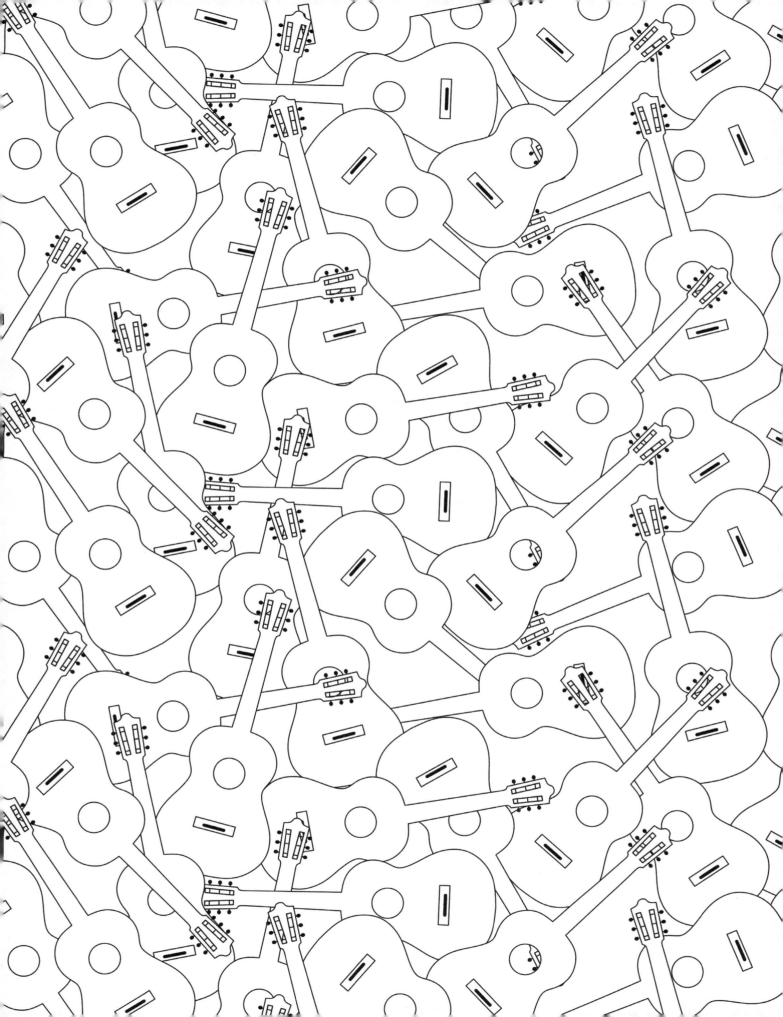

Coming clean

Taylor repeated a surprise song – 'Clean' from *1989* – for the first time during a show in East Rutherford in May 2023 after admitting she should have performed it in a higher key the first time around. During her final performance of 2023, she announced that she would be opening up all of her surprise songs once again for her 2024 dates.

The Midnights era

Sadly, all good things have to come to an end and Taylor brings her Eras Tour shows to a close in style with the *Midnights* act. She kicks off with the dreamy 'Lavender Haze' before taking fans on a journey through her tenth album, performing the likes of 'Anti-Hero' and 'Midnight Rain' and ending with 'Karma'.

Going out in style

Taylor's outfits during the closing *Midnights* chapter are some of the most stunning of the entire show. She brings the curtain down in a fringed bodysuit from designer Oscar de la Renta that was hand-embroidered with over 5,300 crystals and beads, and which took an incredible 315 hours to make!

Record breaking

By the time The Eras Tour comes to an end in Vancouver in December 2024, Taylor will have performed more than 150 shows in over 50 cities across five continents. In December 2023, the tour became the highest-grossing in history after generating an incredible $1 billion in revenue.

Poetry in motion

While accepting her 13th Grammy Award for Best Pop Vocal Album for *Midnights*, Taylor sent Swifties into overdrive as she announced her latest album, *The Tortured Poets Department*. We can't wait to find out which of the album's new songs make it onto the Eras Tour playlist!

The Eras Tour movie

On 13 October 2023, the *Taylor Swift: The Eras Tour* movie was released worldwide. Directed by Sam Wrench, the film gave Swifties who weren't lucky enough to get concert tickets the opportunity to experience the tour in all its glory. It earned over $260 million worldwide at the box office.

Activities

Wordsearches

Quizzes

✓

Tick off the ones you've done!

Spot the difference

Can you find the SIX changes made to the image on the bottom?

Get Taylor to the stage!

Help Taylor sneak past the fans to appear on stage

Setlist scramble

Unscramble these friendship braclets to reveal songs from the Eras Tour setlist

1. A L E C D E T I

2. A M A R K

3. E R O L V

4. G D A A R C I N

5. N E H A M T

6. D C E N T E H N A

Wordsearch

Can you find these 10 Eras Tour acts (plus one Easter egg!) in the puzzle?

```
D S R O U T T K E I T W E V Y
D E K D O O E R A S M O V I E
B S R P H U O T E E T N Q A P
Z X D L R L W X E V V W G E N
S E E G K A U R S W D A J N J
T F E L G U O S O D C G N I R
S A O B G M E N L O C O L N R
T F V T R L K C U B I O B Y C
H S W E R A Z S T T V E N T I
G P V A E P T R A E S U B H G
I E E P K I X T R C S O Z G W
N F S J C P U D A N K X N I B
D F F W U P U X G I Q B I E W
I S K Y E P L Z Z X P P R C N
M Y F R R L F Z B K C N C W G
```

Find these words...

LOVER	REPUTATION	FOLKLORE	MIDNIGHTS
FEARLESS	SPEAKNOW	EIGHTYNINE	
EVERMORE	RED	ACOUSTIC	

Wordsearch

Can you find these nine songs from
the Eras Tour setlist?

I	M	E	V	C	G	Q	X	R	W	L	P	C	N	J
N	M	T	E	Z	W	X	M	O	L	D	D	L	N	J
V	Q	A	P	H	N	X	L	E	D	N	Q	E	F	Y
I	I	C	Z	O	C	L	W	W	Z	V	M	K	E	J
S	N	I	B	G	I	O	P	V	O	E	H	O	V	T
I	R	L	B	W	O	L	E	K	E	E	J	T	Q	N
B	F	E	Y	T	L	U	H	F	W	R	Y	U	N	Y
L	R	D	L	Y	R	O	T	S	E	V	O	L	T	F
E	O	L	P	V	X	M	G	U	T	M	D	P	G	J
S	A	I	K	T	L	U	L	N	Q	C	Y	Y	O	Z	N
T	J	M	L	O	L	F	F	P	A	D	L	V	I	W
R	T	Q	P	A	N	T	I	H	E	R	O	E	P	D
I	C	R	U	E	L	S	U	M	M	E	R	G	O	Q
N	I	X	U	Q	Q	C	O	S	B	D	E	M	O	S
G	Y	P	F	D	E	T	N	A	H	C	N	E	I	P

Find these words...

CRUELSUMMER	DELICATE	INVISIBLESTRING
LOVESTORY	ENCHANTED	STYLE
WILLOW	ALLTOOWELL	ANTIHERO

Wordsearch

Can you find these 10 supporting acts from The Eras Tour?

P	M	I	S	J	L	K	C	U	Z	B	X	K	T	J
H	D	C	U	M	A	U	J	N	P	H	A	I	M	O
O	E	E	S	B	A	X	V	R	K	O	C	I	Q	H
E	R	S	G	K	E	R	G	F	Q	Z	S	S	S	W
B	N	P	K	A	I	A	B	B	A	W	Z	O	K	X
E	I	I	L	B	Y	L	B	A	X	F	N	Q	X	N
B	L	C	I	P	L	L	G	A	E	Y	F	I	P	B
R	R	E	Q	A	K	B	E	Q	D	I	C	V	A	L
I	I	X	B	R	J	W	I	S	D	O	C	R	S	A
D	G	S	G	A	C	D	V	M	I	I	O	A	D	T
G	Y	A	T	M	S	V	K	V	N	Q	E	B	R	Z
E	C	T	F	O	E	Q	R	K	T	U	N	B	E	G
R	W	U	S	R	N	B	A	N	U	M	R	G	Z	E
S	J	O	M	E	V	J	E	R	F	W	J	R	C	J
E	W	L	X	Q	S	A	E	J	L	A	X	I	E	U

Find these words...

PARAMORE	BEABADOOBEE	LOUTA
PHOEBEBRIDGERS	GRACIEABRAMS	ICESPICE
HAIM	GIRLINRED	
GAYLE	MUNA	

89

Quiz

Easy

1. In which American city did The Eras Tour begin?

_____

2. The Eras Tour is Taylor's ...
- [ ] Third
- [ ] Sixth
- [ ] Eighth

... concert tour.

3. How many acts are there in each Eras Tour show?

_____

4. Which is the first act?

_____

5. Which of Taylor's albums is not featured as one of the acts?

_____

6. Finish the lyric of this song from the Eras Tour setlist: *"I would be complex, I would ..."*

_____

7. On average, how long is a standard show of The Eras Tour?
☐ Approx 1hr 30mins
☐ Approx 2hr 30mins
☐ Approx 3hr 30mins

8. Which was the only song from *Speak Now* to originally feature on the standard setlist?

_____

9. How many continents will the Eras Tour visit?

_____

10. What era does Taylor end the show with?

_____

© Getty Images

Quiz

Medium

1. **What was the date of the opening Eras Tour show?**

   _____

2. **Who were the opening acts of the tour's first night?**

   _____

   _____

3. **How many tickets did Taylor sell on the opening day of the US presale?**
   - ☐ 1.5 million
   - ☐ 2.4 million
   - ☐ 3.2 million

4. **How many songs featured in the original standard setlist?**

   _____

5. Which rapper joined Taylor onstage in East Rutherford?

_____

6. Finish the lyric of this song from the Eras Tour setlist: _"A friend to all is a friend to none, Chase two girls, ..."_

_____

7. How many outfit changes has Taylor been known to perform in a night?

_____

8. Which song does The Eras Tour close on?

_____

9. In which city will The Eras Tour conclude in 2024?

_____

10. True or False: The Eras Tour setlist includes the 10-minute version of 'All Too Well'?

☐ True ☐ False

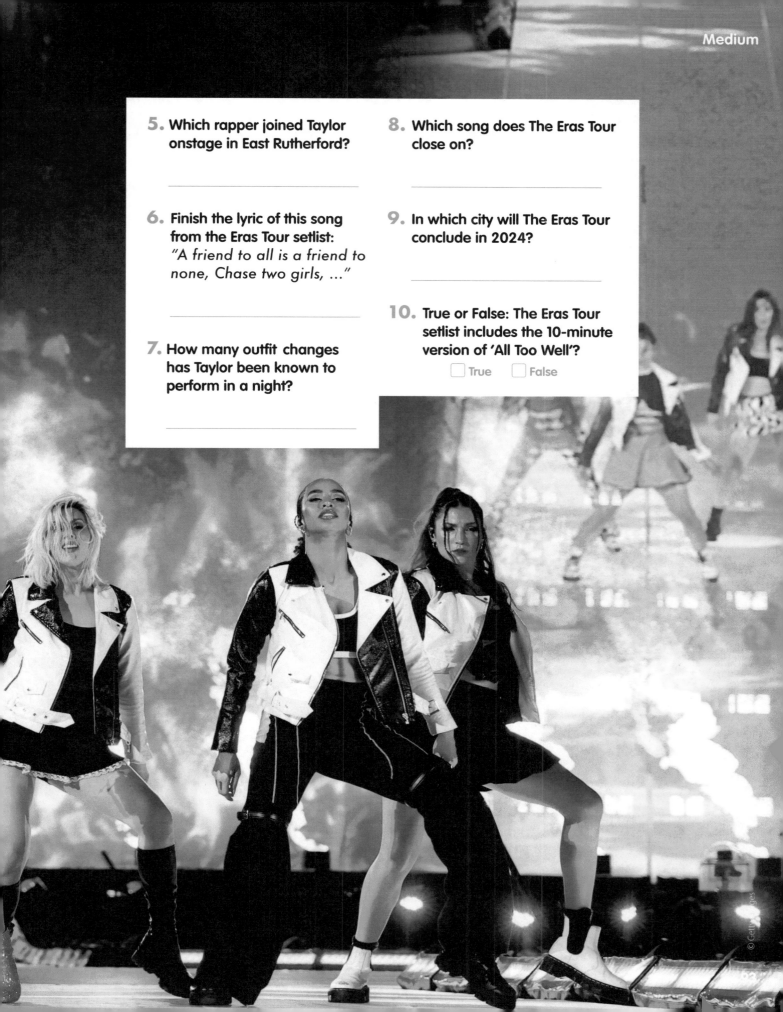

Quiz

Hard

1. In which US city did Swifties cause an earthquake during 'Shake It Off'?

   _____

2. Who decorated Taylor's *Fearless* guitar for the tour?

   _____

3. The Eras Tour became the first concert tour to generate over ___ in revenue
   - [ ] $100 million
   - [ ] $1 billion
   - [ ] $10 billion

4. How many Guinness World Records did The Eras Tour achieve in 2023?

   _____

5. On which TV show did Taylor announce her Eras Tour?

_____

6. Finish the lyric of this song from the Eras Tour setlist: *"You'll see me in hindsight Tangled up with you all night ..."*

_____

_____

7. Who directed the Eras Tour movie?

_____

8. What was the first surprise song to be repeated during the tour?

_____

9. How many shows did Taylor play during the US leg of the tour in 2023?

_____

10. By the end of the tour, which venue will Taylor have performed at the most?

_____

Answers

Get Taylor to the stage

Spot the difference

Setlist Scramble

1. DELICATE
2. KARMA
3. LOVER
4. CARDIGAN
5. THE MAN
6. ENCHANTED

Wordsearches

Secret answer!

Quizzes

Eras Tour acts

```
D S R O U T T K E I T W E V Y
D E K D O O E R A S M O V I E
B S R P H U O T E E T N Q A P
Z X D L R L W X E V V W G E N
S E E G K A U R S W D A J N J
T F E L G U O S O D C G N I R
S A O B G M E N L O C O L N R
T F V T R L K C U B I O B Y C
H S W E R A Z S T T V E N T I
G P V A E P T R A E S U B H G
I E E P K I X T R C S O Z G W
N F S J C P U D A N K X N I B
D F F W U P U X G I Q B I E E
I S K Y E P L Z Z X P P R C N
M Y F R R L F Z B K C N C W G
```

Setlist songs

```
I M E V C G Q X R W L P C N J
N M T E Z W X M O L D D L N J
V Q A P H N X L E D N Q E F Y
I I C Z O C L W W Z V M K E J
S N I B G I O P V O E H O V T
I R L B W O L E K E E J T Q N
B F E Y T L U H F W R Y U N Y
L R D L Y R O T S E V O L T F
E O L P V X M G U T M D P G J
S A I K T U L N Q C Y Y O Z N
T J M L O L F F P A D L V I W
R T Q P A N T I H E R O E P D
I C R U E L S U M M E R G O Q
N I X U Q Q C O S B D E M O S
G Y P F D E T N A H C N E I P
```

Support acts

```
P M I S J L K C U Z B X K T J
H D C U M A U J N P H A I M O
O E E S B A X V R K O C I Q H
E R S G K E R G F Q Z S S S W
B N P K A I A B B A W Z O K X
E I I L B Y L B A X F N Q X E
B L C I P L L G A E Y F I P B
R R E Q A K B E Q D I C V A L
I I X B R J W I S D O C R S A
D G S G A C D V M I I O A D T
G Y A T M S V K V N Q E B R Z
E C T F O E Q R K T U N B E G
R W U S R N B A N U M R G Z E
S J O M E V J E R F W J R C J
E W L X Q S A E J L A X I E U
```

Quizzes

Easy

1. Glendale, Arizona
2. Sixth
3. 10
4. *Lover*
5. Her debut, *Taylor Swift*
6. "Be cool", from 'The Man'
7. Approx 3hr 30mins
8. 'Enchanted'
9. 5
10. *Midnights*

Medium

1. 17 March 2023
2. Paramore and Gayle
3. 2.4 million
4. 44
5. Ice Spice
6. "Lose the one", from 'cardigan'
7. Up to 16
8. 'Karma'
9. Vancouver, Canada
10. True

Hard

1. Seattle
2. Her parents
3. $1 billion
4. 6
5. *Good Morning America*
6. "Burning it down" from 'Wildest Dreams'
7. Sam Wrench
8. 'Clean'
9. 53
10. Wembley, London – 8 times

TAYLOR SWIF
COLOURING & ACTIVITY BOOK *Tou*
Ed

Future PLC Quay House, The Ambury, Bath, BA1 1UA

Editorial
Group Editor **Dan Peel**
Senior Designer **Harriet Knight**
Senior Art Editor **Lora Barnes**
Head of Art & Design **Greg Whitaker**
Editorial Director **Jon White**

Illustrations
Kym Winters

Contributors
Dan Peel

Cover images
Alamy, Getty Images, Kym Winters

Photography
Alamy, Getty
All copyrights and trademarks are recognised and respected

Advertising
Media packs are available on request
Commercial Director **Clare Dove**

International
Head of Print Licensing **Rachel Shaw**
licensing@futurenet.com
www.futurecontenthub.com

Circulation
Head of Newstrade **Tim Mathers**

Production
Head of Production **Mark Constance**
Production Project Manager **Matthew Eglinton**
Advertising Production Manager **Joanne Crosby**
Digital Editions Controller **Jason Hudson**
Production Managers **Keely Miller, Nola Cokely,
Vivienne Calvert, Fran Twentyman**

Printed in the UK

Distributed by Marketforce, 5 Churchill Place, Canary Wharf, London, E14 5HU
www.marketforce.co.uk – For enquiries, please email:
mfcommunications@futurenet.com

Taylor Swift Colouring & Activity Book: Tour Edition First Edition (MUB6299)
© 2024 Future Publishing Limited

FUTURE
Connectors.
Creators.
Experience
Makers.

Future plc is a public
company quoted on the
London Stock Exchange
(symbol: FUTR)
www.futureplc.com

Chief Executive Officer **Jon Steinberg**
Non-Executive Chairman **Richard Huntingford**
Chief Financial and Strategy Officer **Penny Ladkin-Brand**

Tel +44 (0)1225 442 244

Widely
Recycled

ipso. For press freedom
with responsibility

Made in the USA
Columbia, SC
19 December 2024

49871828R00057